WORLD LINK

DEVELOPING ENGLISH FLUENCY

FOURTH EDITION
WORKBOOK

WORLD
LINK INTRO
DEVELOPING ENGLISH FLUENCY

NATIONAL GEOGRAPHIC
LEARNING

Australia · Brazil · Canada · Mexico · Singapore · United Kingdom · United States

National Geographic Learning,
a Cengage Company

World Link Level Intro Workbook
Fourth Edition

Publisher: Sherrise Roehr

Executive Editor: Sarah Kenney

Managing Editor: Claudi Mimó

Development Editor: Adam Robinson

Director of Global Marketing: Ian Martin

Heads of Regional Marketing:
  Charlotte Ellis (Europe, Middle East
  and Africa)
  Irina Pereyra (Latin America)

Senior Product Marketing Manager:
  Caitlin Thomas

Content Project Manager: Beth Houston

Media Researcher: Stephanie
  Eenigenburg

Cover/Text Design: Lisa Trager

Art Director: Brenda Carmichael

Operations Support: Hayley Chwazik-Gee,
  Avi Mednick

Manufacturing Planner: Mary Beth
  Hennebury

Composition: MPS North America LLC

For permission to use material from this text or product,
submit all requests online at **cengage.com/permissions**
Further permissions questions can be emailed to
permissionrequest@cengage.com

ISBN: 978-0-357-50366-9

National Geographic Learning
200 Pier 4 Boulevard
Boston, MA 02210
USA

Locate your local office at **international.cengage.com/region**

Visit National Geographic Learning online at **ELTNGL.com**
Visit our corporate website at **www.cengage.com**

Printed in the United States of America
Print Number: 02 Print Year: 2024

TABLE OF CONTENTS

PHOTO CREDITS

1 INTRODUCTIONS

VOCABULARY

A   Complete the sentences. Use the words in the box.

David	Mr.	Smith	teacher

1. He is a _____.

2. His first name is _____.

3. His last name is _____.

4. In class, we call him _____ Smith.

B   Write the numbers from the box next to the correct words.

0	1	2	4	7	8

1. _____ seven   3. _____ zero   5. _____ two

2. _____ four   4. _____ eight   6. _____ one

C   Complete the sentences. Use the words in the box.

classmate	email	first	last	nickname	phone number

1. My _____ name is Tomas.

2. Her _____ name is Lopez.

3. What's your _____ address?

4. His _____ is (472) 615–7823.

5. My name is Alicia, but my _____ is Ali.

6. She's my _____.

D   Complete the information about yourself.

1. First name: _____

2. Last name: _____

3. Nickname: _____

4. Phone Number: _____

5. Email: _____

CONVERSATION

A   Complete the sentences with the contracted forms of the words in parentheses.

1. **A:** Hi, (I am) _____ Maya.

   B: (It is) _____ nice to meet you.

2. **A:** Who is he?

   B: (He is) _____ my friend.

3. **A:** Who is she?

   B: (She is) _____ my teacher.

4. **A:** (What is) _____ that?

   B: (It is) _____ a dictionary.

B   Number the sentences in order to make conversations.

1. _____   Yes, I am.

   _1_   Hello. My name is Mrs. Lane.

   _____   Nice to meet you, Mrs. Lane. My name is Yukiko.

   _____   Are you a student in my class?

2. _____   Hi. I'm Ming. Is Carlos your last name?

   _____   How do you spell Diaz?

   _____   Hello. I'm Carlos.

   _____   No, it's my first name. My last name is Diaz.

   _____   D–I–A–Z.

3. _____   It's nice to meet you, Kenjiro.

   _____   Hi. What's your name?

   _____   It's nice to meet you, too.

   _____   I'm Kenjiro.

C   Write two more conversations.

You: _____

Your classmate: _____

You: _____

Your classmate: _____

You: _____

You: _____

Your teacher: _____

You: _____

Your teacher: _____

You: _____

GRAMMAR

A Complete the sentences. Use the words in the box. You can use the words more than once.

am	are	is

1. It _____ my book.

2. She _____ the teacher.

3. I _____ Tina.

4. They _____ my classmates.

5. You _____ a student.

B Rewrite the underlined sentences correctly.

1. She is a teacher. <u>My name is Mrs. Lee.</u>

   Her name is Mrs. Lee.

2. You are my classmate. <u>Her first name is Linda.</u>

   _____

3. Carlos is a student. <u>Its last name is Diaz.</u>

   _____

4. I'm Jake. <u>His email address is jake28@easypost.com.</u>

   _____

5. Please call me Tino. <u>It's his nickname.</u>

   _____

C Choose the correct words to complete the sentences.

1. _____ a student at the University of Campinas.	a. I'm	b. My
2. _____ Carole.	a. I'm	b. My
3. _____ name is Cassandra.	a. You're	b. Your
4. _____ Daniel.	a. You're	b. Your
5. _____ Abdul.	a. His	b. He's
6. _____ a baseball player.	a. His	b. He's
7. _____ name is Zara.	a. She's	b. Her
8. _____ very happy today.	a. She's	b. Her
9. _____ teachers.	a. Their	b. They're
10. _____ names are Marta and Claude.	a. Their	b. They're

VOCABULARY AND GRAMMAR

A Match the questions and answers.

_a_ 1. Are they students in our class?

_____ 2. Is Rihanna a soccer player?

_____ 3. Is your favorite kind of music hip-hop?

_____ 4. Is your favorite sport swimming?

_____ 5. Is Carlos from Mexico?

_____ 6. Am I in your class?

_____ 7. Is Beyonce your favorite singer?

a. No, they're not.

b. No, he isn't. He's from Cuba.

c. Yes, it is.

d. No, it isn't. It's basketball.

e. No, she isn't. She's a singer.

f. No, she isn't. It's Ariana Grande.

g. Yes, you are.

B Read the chart. Then answer the questions.

Name	Frank Hong	Sue Parker	Ricardo Sanchez
Favorite music	hip-hop	pop and dance	dance
Favorite movie	*Spider-Man: Far From Home*	*Mulan*	*Avengers: Endgame*
Favorite sport	basketball	swimming	soccer

1. Is Sue's favorite sport soccer? *No, it isn't. It's swimming.* _____

2. Are Sue's favorite kinds of music pop and dance? _____

3. Is Ricardo's favorite kind of music hip-hop? _____

4. Is Ricardo's favorite sport soccer? _____

5. Is Frank's favorite movie *Captain Marvel*? _____

6. Is Frank's favorite sport tennis? _____

C Complete the chart with your own information.

Name	
Favorite music	
Favorite movie	
Favorite sport	

1. Is your favorite kind of music classical? _____

2. Is your favorite movie *The Lion King*? _____

3. Is your favorite sport baseball? _____

READING AND WRITING

A Read the article.

English Nicknames

Nicknames are very popular in English!

Some nicknames are female. Cathy is a nickname for Catherine. Sue is a nickname for Susan. Liz, Lizzy, Beth, Bess, and Betty are all nicknames for Elizabeth!

Men also have nicknames. Bob and Rob are nicknames for Robert, and Mike is a nickname for Michael.

Some nicknames are both male and female. Chris is a nickname for Christine. It's also a nickname for Christopher.

Do you have a nickname? What is it?

His real name is William Arthur Philip Louis. He is the Duke of Cambridge, but his family calls him Wills.

Her real name is Catherine Elizabeth Middleton. She is the Duchess of Cambridge, but her family and friends call her Kate.

B Write short answers.

1. Is Michael a nickname? _____

2. Are Liz and Cathy female nicknames? _____

3. Is Rob a male nickname? _____

4. Is Sue a nickname for Elizabeth? _____

5. Are nicknames popular in your country? _____

C Write the nicknames next to the names.

Male names	Nickname(s)	Female names	Nickname(s)
Robert	_____	Susan	_____
Michael	_____	Elizabeth	_____
Christopher	_____	Catherine	_____

D Circle the correct answer.

His name **(1.) am / is / are** Yoshihiko Sato. Everyone **(2.) calls / what's / meets** him Yoshi. **(3.) He's / His / Him** a student. **(4.) He's / His / Him** phone number is 631-555-8763. His email **(5.) name / number / address** is sato92@nihon.net. His favorite sport is soccer, and his favorite type of **(6.) music / movie / TV show** is rock.

E Write about a friend or family member. Include his or her favorite movie, TV show, music, singer or band, sport, or sports player.

_____

_____

_____

_____

_____

_____

_____

F Think about a famous person from your country. Write about three of his or her favorite things.

_____

_____

_____

_____

_____

_____

_____

② COUNTRIES

AROUND THE WORLD

VOCABULARY

A Choose the correct answer.

1. Yusef is from Ankara, **Turkish** / **Turkey**.
2. Diego is from **Brazil** / **Brazilian**.
3. Mei Li is **China** / **Chinese**.
4. The capital of **Peruvian** / **Peru** is Lima.
5. Ji Ming is from Seoul. She's **Korea** / **Korean**.
6. Ryan is from Canberra. He's **Australian** / **Australia**.
7. Montreal is a city in **Canada** / **Canadian**.
8. Peter is from Kingston. He's **Jamaican** / **Jamaica**.

B Complete the sentences with the correct nationality or language.

1. Monica is from the UK.

   She's _____.

2. I'm Japanese.

   I speak _____.

3. Mateo is from Mexico City.

   He's _____.

4. Ana is from Spain.

   She speaks _____.

5. Greg is from the United States.

   He's _____.

6. Fernanda is from Portugal.

   She's _____.

C Match the words. Write the letter of the answer on the line.

_____ **1.** Beijing   a. capital

_____ **2.** English   b. country

_____ **3.** Australian   c. language

_____ **4.** Brazil   d. nationality

CONVERSATION

A Unscramble the words to make a conversation. Remember to use correct punctuation and capitalization.

A: Stefan / I'm / hi

_____ .

B: Stefan / from / hi / are / where / you

_____ ?

A: from / Santiago, Chile / I'm

_____ .

B: capital / Santiago / of / the / Chile / is

_____ ?

A: is / it / yes

_____ .

B Complete the conversations.

1. **Valencia, Spain**

   A: Where are you **(1.)** _____?

   B: I'm from Spain.

   A: Really? Which city?

   B: **(2.)** _____ from Valencia.

   A: Is that the capital of **(3.)** _____?

   B: No, it **(4.)** _____ . Madrid is the capital.

2. **Your hometown, your country**

   A: (1.) _Where are you from?_ _____

   B: (2.) _____

   A: (3.) _____

   B: (4.) _____

   A: (5.) _____

   B: (6.) _____

C Match the question parts. Write the letter of the answer on the line.

_____ 1. Where are   a. Peru?

_____ 2. Which   b. exactly?

_____ 3. Are you   c. you from?

_____ 4. Where in   d. from Peru?

_____ 5. Where   e. city?

GRAMMAR

A Choose the correct word to complete each question.

1. Hello? _____ is this?

  a. Who's

  b. Where

  c. Who

2. _____ are you?

  a. Who's

  b. Where

  c. Where's

3. You're in France? _____ in France?

  a. Where

  b. Where's

  c. Who's

4. _____ with you?

  a. Where

  b. Who

  c. Who's

B Complete the conversation. Use *in*, *at*, and *from*.

A: Oh, Maria! Hello. Where are you?

B: I'm (1.) _____ Mexico. Lisa is with me.

A: Who's Lisa? Where is she (2.) _____?

B: She's my Australian friend. She's (3.) _____ Sydney.
We're (4.) _____ the beach today.

A: And where is this beach?

B: It's (5.) _____ Cancun. We're on vacation in Mexico!

C Complete the sentences. Use the words in the box.

at	in	where's	who	who's

1. _____ is this?

2. _____ your school?

3. Are you _____ home now?

4. _____ with you?

5. Is Andy _____ New York?

D Match the questions and answers.

_____ 1. Who's in La Paz?

_____ 2. Where's your friend from?

_____ 3. Where is dad?

_____ 4. Who's in the gym right now?

_____ 5. Where's Riyadh?

_____ 6. Where are Alex and Mia?

a. It's in Saudi Arabia.

b. He's at work.

c. Felipe is. He has an exercise class.

d. She's from Moscow.

e. They're in the classroom.

f. Nicolas is.

VOCABULARY AND GRAMMAR

A Write the adjectives for cities in the chart. Use your opinions.

beautiful	busy	famous	interesting	old	small
big	crowded	friendly	large	popular	tall
boring	exciting	fun	new	relaxing	wonderful

Good ☺	OK ☺	Bad ☹

B What do you think these cities are like? Write sentences. Give your own ideas for the last two.

1. Washington, DC _Washington, DC is famous and interesting._

2. São Paulo _____

3. Tokyo _____

4. Paris _____

5. Dubai _____

6. _____ _____

7. _____ _____

C Complete the sentences with *is*, *isn't*, *are*, and *aren't*.

1. There are a lot of people in the city. It _____ very crowded.

2. My city is exciting. It _____ boring.

3. The streets are very old. They _____ new.

4. The people here always say hello. They _____ friendly.

5. My town _____ very large. It's small.

D Complete the sentences about your hometown. Use your own ideas.

1. My town is _____.

2. People in my hometown aren't _____.

READING AND WRITING

A Read the article. Match the cities in the box with the descriptions.

Brasilia	New York City	Oxford	Seoul	Rome

Name the City

1. _____

   This is a very big city! It's in North America. There are many museums and art galleries. It's busy and exciting.

2. _____

   It's the capital of a country. It's in South America. The buildings are big and new. There are many parks.

3. _____

   This is a small, old English city. There's a famous university, and 30,000 students from many countries live here.

4. _____

   This city is very old. It's crowded, but the buildings are very beautiful. There are lots of interesting neighborhoods.

5. _____

   This is a crowded capital city in Asia. It has a lot of new, tall buildings. It is famous for modern technology.

park

museum

building

B Answer the questions. Use your own opinions.

1. Which city is good for a vacation? _____

   Why? _____

   _____

   _____

2. Which city is bad for a vacation? _____

   Why? _____

   _____

   _____

C Read the travel ad. Cross out the eight spelling mistakes. Write the correct spelling above them. Use the example to help you.

Vacation
Vacation
Spend Your ~~Vacattion~~ in Oslo!

Why?

- It's the capatal of the country.
- It has big, beutiful parks.
- It's not croded and it's very new.
- The people are friendley.
- The beaches are lagre and rilaxing.

Visit:

- The National Museum
- Vigeland Park
- Many intresting small islands
- The Royal Palace
- Holmenkollen Ski Museum

When:

- It's best to go in spring or sumer.

See you soon!

D Write a travel ad for your favorite city.

_____

_____

_____

_____

_____

_____

_____

_____

3 POSSESSIONS

A GIFTS

VOCABULARY

A Match the sentence halves.

1. I'm wearing my new
2. My notebook is in my
3. I have my credit cards in my
4. I listen to music with my
5. We have two gift
6. I do my homework on my
7. The sun hurts my eyes. I need my
8. I want to go out tonight. Let's buy

a. headphones.
b. wallet.
c. movie tickets.
d. laptop.
e. cards.
f. watch.
g. backpack.
h. sunglasses.

B Complete the sentences with the words in the box.

| giftcard | laptop | sunglasses | wallet | watch |

1. Some people don't wear a _____ because they use their phone to check the time.
2. Oh, no! I don't have money. I forgot my _____!
3. I like to wear _____ when I'm at the beach.
4. She wants a restaurant _____ for her birthday.
5. I use my _____ to study and to work.

C Answer the questions. Use complete sentences.

1. What is your favorite possession? Why? _____

_____

_____

2. Is it expensive? _____

_____

3. Is it a gift from a friend? _____

_____

4. Would you give it as a gift to someone else? Why? _____

_____

_____

CONVERSATION

A Circle the correct phrase to complete each conversation.

1. **A:** Thanks so much!

   B: Excuse me. / (No problem) / No, it isn't.

2. **A: Who is it? / Is this your wallet? / What's your name?**

   B: Yes, it is. Thanks!

3. **A: Is that your backpack? / Thanks for the gift. / What's this?**

   B: You're welcome.

4. **A: Thank you. / Excuse me. / Are these your headphones?**

   B: No, they aren't.

5. **A: Thanks so much. / Excuse me. / It's a gift card.**

   B: My pleasure.

B Number the sentences in order to make a conversation.

_____ The movie tickets! Where are they?

_____ What's wrong, Pedro?

_____ No, they aren't in my wallet . . .

_____ Are they in your wallet?

_____ Yes! Thank you very much!

_____ Excuse me, sir. Are these your tickets?

C Are these expressions formal (F) or informal (I)?

_____ **1.** Thank you very much.   _____ **4.** You're welcome.

_____ **2.** You bet.   _____ **5.** Sure, no problem.

_____ **3.** My pleasure.   _____ **6.** Thanks a lot.

D Write your own conversations.

1. **A:** _____

   B: _____

   A: You bet.

2. **A:** _____

   B: You're welcome.

3. **A:** Excuse me. _____

   B: _____

   A: _____

4. **A:** Is this your _____

   B: _____

5. **A:** _____

   B: No problem.

GRAMMAR

A Write the plural forms.

1. notebook _____
2. country _____
3. camera _____
4. cell phone _____
5. dish _____
6. dictionary _____

7. watch _____
8. key _____
9. bus pass _____
10. backpack _____
11. leaf _____
12. wife _____

B Circle the correct plural form of each word.

1. **knife**

   a. knifes   b. knive   c. knives

2. **tomato**

   a. tomatoes   b. tomatos   c. tomaties

3. **man**

   a. mans   b. men   c. manes

4. **child**

   a. children   b. childies   c. childs

5. **photo**

   a. photos   b. photoes   c. photones

6. **class**

   a. class   b. classen   c. classes

C Circle the words that are in the plural form.

cities	class	dictionary	pictures
umbrellas	people	actress	email address
exercise	friends	women	bus pass

D What's in your wallet or bag? Use correct articles and plural forms.

_____
_____
_____
_____
_____
_____

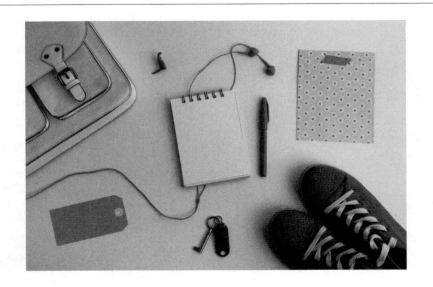

B IMPORTANT ITEMS

VOCABULARY AND GRAMMAR

A Write the opposite of each word.

1. important _____

2. clean _____

3. easy _____

4. expensive _____

5. good _____

B Complete the sentences with the correct forms of *be* and *this*, *that*, *these*, or *those*.

1. _____*Is*_____ _____*this*_____ your backpack?

2. _____ _____ your keys?

3. _____ _____ your teacher? (over there)

4. _____ _____ your headphones? (over there)

5. _____ _____ Erin's umbrella?

6. _____ _____ his notebook?

7. _____ _____ my sunglasses? (over there)

C Unscramble the words to make sentences. In some cases, there may be more than one correct answer.

1. gift / that's / an / expensive

   _____.

2. good / cell / phone / is / this / a

   _____.

3. excellent / these / headphones / are

   _____.

4. music / terrible / is / this

   _____.

5. those / cheap / are / tickets / movie

   _____.

D Look around the room. Write sentences using the words in **A**.

1. *Those are expensive sunglasses.* _____

2. _____

3. _____

4. _____

5. _____

READING AND WRITING

A Read this ad and fill in the products.

The Megastore Holiday Sale is here!

1. _____ *laptop* _____
The new LC-009 is light-weight and has a long-life battery. Easy to use. $2,000.

2. _____
Enjoy your music on the go with these wireless BT-333s. Clean, clear sound. $20.

3. _____
Know what time it is, in style with the WX-240. Cheap. Only $75.

4. _____
Make video calls, take excellent photos, and download hundreds of apps with the huge memory. The CL-260. Everyone wants one. Now only $400.

5. _____

The Hikemate 2 is every traveler's best friend. It's comfortable and waterproof. It keeps your important things clean and safe. Only $45.

B Circle **T** for *true* or **F** for *false*. Rewrite the false sentences to make them true.

1. The LC-009 is hard to use. T   F

_____

2. The BT-333s have messy wires. T   F

_____

3. The WX-240 is expensive. T   F

_____

4. The CL-260 is popular. T   F

_____

5. The Hikemate 2 is uncomfortable. T   F

_____

C Read the email. Unscramble the letters to make words. Use **A** and **B** to help you, if necessary.

Hi, Ben!

Thank you for the **(1.)** _____ (phnesdheao). They're great! They're the

(2.) _____ (prfctee) birthday gift for me. They're really **(3.)** _____ (yeas)

to use and the sound is very good! These are very **(4.)** _____ (nepsiveex).

I feel bad because I always buy you cheap gifts. Anyway, I think they're

(5.) _____ (entlexlec). Thanks a lot!

See you!

Vera

D Read the email. Correct the eight spelling and grammar errors.

Hi, Jorge!

How are you? Do you like your new college?

I am cleaning your room right now because it is so mesy! I want to throw away some old things.

Look at theze photos. Are this your sunglasses? They look very cheep. Do you want to kip

them? Also, there is a laptp under your bed. It is important to have a good computer at college!

Do you want me to bring it when I visit next week? And do you need this three books? They're

expensve!

I can't wait to see you!

Love,

Mom

E Write an email to your friend about your favorite electronic product.

_____

_____

_____

_____

_____

_____

_____

_____

4 ACTIVITIES

A WHAT ARE YOU DOING?

VOCABULARY

A Unscramble the letters to complete the present continuous verbs.

1. p o s h p   <u>s</u> <u>h</u> <u>o</u> <u>p</u> <u>p</u> ing   6. s c e r e i x   __ __ __ __ __ __ __ ing

2. c h a t w   __ __ __ __ __ ing   7. k i n r d   __ __ __ __ __ ing

3. n i s t l e   __ __ __ __ __ __ ing   8. a e t   __ __ __ ing

4. k a l t   __ __ __ __ ing   9. d y s u t   __ __ __ __ __ ing

5. t t x e   __ __ __ __ ing   10. o g   __ __ ing

B Complete each sentence with the correct preposition. Use *to*, *for*, or *on*. Write *X* if no preposition is needed.

1. She's eating _____<u>X</u>_____ breakfast now.

2. They're studying _____ a test.

3. He's eating _____ pizza.

4. She's doing _____ her homework.

5. Mila is texting _____ her sister.

6. Marco is talking _____ the phone.

7. He is talking _____ his son.

8. Ming is listening _____ music.

C Complete the sentences with the correct forms of the verbs in the box. Use each word only once.

drink	eat	exercise	go	listen	study	talk	watch

1. Katrina is _____ to jazz music.

2. They're _____ Korean food.

3. She's _____ soccer on TV.

4. Pedro is _____ to his friends.

5. Dad is _____ coffee.

6. Linda is _____ to class.

7. They're _____ at the gym.

8. We're _____ for an exam.

CONVERSATION

A   Number the sentences in order to make a conversation.

_____ Sorry to hear that.

_____ Hi, Lukas. How are you doing?

_____ So-so.

__1__ Hello?

_____ Hey, Tina. It's Lukas.

_____ Fine. How about you?

_____ Yeah? What's wrong?

_____ I'm studying for a test and don't understand the questions.

B   Unscramble the words to make a conversation. Remember to use correct punctuation and capitalization.

A: doing / you / how / hi / are

_____ ?

B: good / about / you / how / pretty

_____ ?

A: fine / I'm / what / doing / you / are

_____ ?

B: exercising / park / at / the / I'm

_____ .

A: how / sister / your / is

_____ ?

B: so-so / studying / she's / for / English test / an

_____ .

C   Write a conversation like the ones in **A** and **B**. Use your own ideas.

A: _____

B: _____

A: _____

B: _____

A: _____

B: _____

A: _____

B: _____

GRAMMAR

A   Write sentences. Use the present continuous. Use contractions when possible.

1. Elena / study English   *Elena is studying English.* _____

2. Carlos / not write emails _____

3. They / listen to music _____

4. Mindy / talk on the phone _____

5. We / not eat French food _____

6. Rio / not watch TV _____

7. I / not do homework _____

8. Mohammad / text Alison _____

B   Write questions.

1. you / eat dinner   *Are you eating dinner?* _____

2. John / play tennis _____

3. she / listen to hip-hop _____

4. Mr. and Mrs. Sosa / exercise _____

5. you / watch a movie _____

6. we / study English _____

C   Look at the office schedule and answer the questions.

University Admissions Office	Daily Schedule Monday, June 4
Staff	**Task**
Frank	Answer emails
Linda & Claudia	Meet with Mr. Pak
Joe	Update the website
Rosa	Talk to new students
David	Write reports
Ahmed	Answer phones

1. What's Frank doing today? _____

2. Is Joe updating the website? _____

3. What's Rosa doing today? _____

4. What are Linda and Claudia doing? _____

5. Is David writing emails today? _____

6. Who is answering the phones? _____

VOCABULARY AND GRAMMAR

A Unscramble these school subjects and college majors. At least one letter is already in each word.

1. u r g n i n s   n _ _ _ _ _ _ _
2. h a m t   _ _ _ h
3. w a l   _ _ w

4. r a t   _ _ t
5. s n u b s i e s   _ u _ _ _ _ s _
6. c i n e s c e   _ c _ _ _ _ _

B Unscramble the words to make statements or questions.

1. you / are / English / why / studying

    *Why are you studying English*_____?

2. preparing / he's / law school / for / entrance exam / the

    _____.

3. for / science / studying / the / we're / test

    _____.

4. these days / you / are / where / living

    _____?

5. art / a project / for / class / working on / I'm

    _____.

6. study / planning / she's / to / business

    _____.

7. majoring / engineering / in / they're

    _____.

8. am / class / taking / art / I / an

    _____?

C Complete the sentences with the present continuous. Then circle *right now* or *these days*.

1. I _____ (visit) Iceland this month.   right now   these days
2. My brother _____ (start) a new job this week.   right now   these days
3. Shh! We _____ (watch) a movie.   right now   these days
4. She _____ (talk) to Barbara.   right now   these days
5. I _____ (study) Spanish in school.   right now   these days
6. I _____ (enjoy) my classes this year.   right now   these days
7. Wait one moment. I _____ (text) Andrea.   right now   these days
8. They _____ (learn) a lot from their teacher.   right now   these days

READING AND WRITING

A Read the article.

International Students Enjoy Summer Classes

Hiroko

I'm from Osaka, Japan. I'm majoring in information technology, but this summer I'm just studying English—six hours a day! I also joined the tennis club, and I'm playing tennis every day. It's great. I'm meeting lots of Americans.

Felix

I'm from Berlin, the capital of Germany. My major is nursing. This summer, I'm taking three classes at the university—English, math, and engineering. I'm really busy! After class, I like listening to music.

Gisele

I'm from São Paulo, Brazil, and I'm an art major. I'm taking two art classes in summer school. There is a lot of homework. I'm working very hard this summer! To relax, I'm taking a yoga class.

B Complete the chart with information from the article in **A**.

Name	Nationality	Major	Subjects	Free time
	Japanese			
		nursing		
				yoga

C Read the study-abroad postcard. Fill in the blanks with the correct forms of the words in the box.

drink	eat	go	listen	shop	study	take	watch

Dear Yasmeen,

Hello from Italy! I'm here with my class. Right now, we're **(1.)** _____ coffee and **(2.)** _____ gelato in a great little cafe near the Colosseum. We're **(3.)** _____ to wonderful local music and **(4.)** _____ people walk by. This week, we're **(5.)** _____ art here in Rome. Next week, we're **(6.)** _____ to Florence! We're **(7.)** _____ a train there. But while we're still here, we're **(8.)** _____ for fashionable Italian clothes!

See you!

Malti

PLACE
STAMP
HERE

D Now imagine your study-abroad experience. Write a postcard to a friend.

PLACE
STAMP
HERE

FOOD

A WHAT'S ON THE MENU?

VOCABULARY

A Write the food words.

1. __ __ __ __ __

3. rice and __ __ __ __ __ __

5. __ __ __ __ __ __

2. __ __ __ __ __ __ __ __

4. __ __ __ __ __

6. __ __ __ __ __ __

B Match the words.

_____ 1. a baked   a. chicken

_____ 2. spinach   b. soup

_____ 3. fried   c. salad

_____ 4. a burger   d. and fries

_____ 5. a tuna fish   e. potato

_____ 6. vegetable   f. sandwich

C Look at the foods in **A**. Which do you like? Write sentences.

I like to eat bread and soup.

_____

_____

_____

_____

_____

CONVERSATION

A Put the sentences in the correct order to make conversations.

1.

_____ Are you hungry?

_____ Let's go to China Garden. They have great food.

_____ Yes, I love it.

_____ Yes, I am.

_____ Do you like Chinese food?

2.

_____ That's OK. They have chicken and pasta, too.

_____ Sounds good!

_____ Well, I don't really like pizza.

_____ Let's go to Pizza Paradise for dinner.

3.

_____ Then let's go to Tito's Mexican Restaurant.

_____ I'm hungry, too. Let's have dinner.

_____ Do you like tacos?

_____ I'm hungry!

_____ Yes, I like them a lot.

B Complete the conversation with the words in the box.

hungry	Indian	juice	kind	love	restaurant

A: I'm **(1.)** _____.

B: Me, too.

A: What **(2.)** _____ of food do you want to eat?

B: Well, I really like **(3.)** _____ food. Do you like it?

A: I **(4.)** _____ it!

B: Great. I know a good **(5.)** _____ we can go to. They have delicious Naan bread.

A: Let's go there.

C Now write your own conversation.

A: _____

B: _____

A: _____

B: _____

A: _____

GRAMMAR

A Complete the sentences with the correct forms of the verbs in the box.

| do | drink | exercise | go | have | know | study | teach |

1. We _____ fruit and coffee for breakfast.

2. Man-Ho _____ law at the university.

3. I _____ my homework every day.

4. The students _____ to the library.

5. Nami _____ five cups of tea every day.

6. Laura _____ at the gym after class.

7. Mr. Suarez _____ Spanish.

8. They _____ a good Vietnamese restaurant.

B Make the sentences negative.

1. I eat breakfast every day. _____

2. Carmen studies Japanese. _____

3. We make pasta every Saturday night. _____

4. Young-Mi drinks coffee. _____

5. My friends order pizza on Fridays. _____

6. I like vegetable soup. _____

7. Johan speaks Mandarin well. _____

8. My aunt works in an office. _____

C Write true sentences with these verbs.

1. do   *I do homework.* _____

You:

2. listen _____

3. no / eat _____

4. talk _____

5. no / make _____

Your friend:

6. have _____

7. go _____

8. no / study _____

9. drink _____

VOCABULARY AND GRAMMAR

A Complete the sentences with the words in the box.

bad for you	energy	high in	low in	meal	snack	tastes good

1. Eating too much of anything can be _____.

2. A piece of fruit between meals is a healthy _____.

3. Breakfast is an important _____. Don't skip it!

4. The food you eat gives you _____.

5. Some coffee drinks are very _____ sugar.

6. I think fruit salad _____, and it's good for you.

7. Vegetables are _____ sugar.

B Write questions and short answers.

1. you / like / vegetables   *Do you like vegetables?*
   yes   *Yes, I do.*

2. your mother / cook / every day
   no

3. your friends / eat / healthy meals
   yes

4. cheese / taste / good
   yes

5. you / eat / foods high in sugar
   no

6. Andrea / eat / unhealthy snacks
   no

C Write questions and answers about people you know. Use *like* and different foods.

1. _____Rita_____   **Q:** *Does Rita like rice?*
                        A: *Yes, she does.*

2. _____   **Q:** _____
                        A: _____

3. _____   **Q:** _____
                        A: _____

4. _____   **Q:** _____
                        A: _____

READING AND WRITING

A   Read the article. Write the correct number for each photo.

What's Your Diet Like?

1. I live in Istanbul, Turkey. My favorite food is fried
chicken. I also like cookies and cake. I eat too much
food that is high in sugar, but it's so delicious! I also like
some healthy foods, especially spinach and beans. I eat
any food that tastes good to me.

—Ali Aslan

2. I eat only healthy foods, like vegetable soup and rice
dishes. I also eat a lot of fish. In Japan, it's easy to find
foods like these. I don't drink fruit juice or soda—just
water. Do I like eating this way? No, I don't. But I need to
lose weight. I'm on a diet.

—Kenji Ono

3. I take a lot of vitamins. I want to be healthy, so I watch
what I eat. Mostly I have salads—fruit salad, vegetable
salad, chicken salad—any salad is fine with me. I live in
Mexico, but I never eat tacos. And I never eat junk food.
Sometimes I drink smoothies. They taste good, and
they're good for me.

—Marta Diaz

B   Complete the chart.

Name	Country	Foods	Why?
			He thinks they're delicious. They taste good.
Kenji Ono			
		salads smoothies	

C Write the correct forms of the verbs in parentheses.

My health habits are good. I **(1.)** _____ (eat) breakfast every day.

I **(2.)** _____ (not, skip) meals, and I **(3.)** _____ (not, drink) soda.

I **(4.)** _____ (exercise) a lot, and I **(5.)** _____ (play) tennis.

I **(6.)** _____ (not, eat) a lot of junk food, but I **(7.)** _____ (love) ice cream.

I **(8.)** _____ (sleep) eight hours every night. I **(9.)** _____ (take) care of my health.

Toshi **(10.)** _____ (be) my best friend. He's very different from me.

Toshi **(11.)** _____ (not, take) care of his health. He **(12.)** _____ (not, exercise).

He **(13.)** _____ (skip) meals a lot, and he **(14.)** _____ (not, eat) breakfast.

He **(15.)** _____ (eat) junk food all day. He **(16.)** _____ (study) very hard,

and he only **(17.)** _____ (sleep) for four hours every night. I'm worried about Toshi!

D Write sentences about your health habits. Are they good, OK, or not so good?

_____

_____

_____

_____

_____

_____

_____

_____

_____

_____

_____

_____

_____

_____

6
RELATIONSHIPS

A FAMILY

VOCABULARY

A Write each word in the correct box.

| aunt | cousin | father | grandmother | mother | sister | uncle |
| brother | daughter | grandfather | grandparents | parent | son | |

Male	**Female**	**Male or Female**

B Match the sentence parts.

1. Your mother's father is your
2. Your sister's mother is your
3. Your mother's brother is your
4. Your father's mother is your
5. Your mother and father are your
6. Your father's sister is your
7. Your parents' parents are your
8. Your uncle's children are your

   a. mother.
   b. parents.
   c. grandparents.
   d. grandfather.
   e. aunt.
   f. cousins.
   g. uncle.
   h. grandmother.

C Write sentences about your family.

There are five people in my family. Nino is my older brother.

D Write the numbers in words.

1. 93 _____ninety-three_____
2. 77 _____
3. 80 _____
4. 46 _____
5. 25 _____

6. 32 _____
7. 64 _____
8. 18 _____
9. 58 _____
10. 12 _____

CONVERSATION

A A reporter is asking Lori Smith about her family. Unscramble the words to make questions and answers.

1. this / person / who / is

   Reporter: _____?

   my / sister / that's / younger

   Lori: _____.

2. old / sister / is / how / your

   Reporter: _____?

   old / 15 / she's / years

   Lori: _____.

3. are / your / these / brothers

   Reporter: _____?

   they're / brothers / yes, / my

   Lori: _____.

4. they / are / age / same / the

   Reporter: _____?

   is / no, / brother / Kevin / my / older

   Lori: _____.

B Write an interview about your family. Use your own ideas.

Reporter: _____

_____

You: _____

_____

Reporter: _____

_____

You: _____

_____

Reporter: _____

_____

You: _____

_____

Reporter: _____

_____

You: _____

_____

GRAMMAR

A Read the chart and complete the sentences with what these people have.

Do you have a... ?	Charles	Shelly	The Parks
watch	no	yes	no
cell phone	yes (this year!)	no	no
car	no	yes (Ford)	yes (Toyota)
daughter	no	yes (name: Mia)	no
son	yes (name: Rex)	no	yes (name: Lee)

1. Lee is _____ son.

2. _____ cell phone is new.

3. _____ car is Japanese.

4. _____ watch is nice.

5. _____ son is named Rex.

6. _____ daughter is friendly.

B James and Sarah have two children, Annie and Jeff. Complete the sentences about their family using the information in the picture.

1. Sarah is _____ wife.

   She is _____ grandmother.

2. Annie is _____ sister.

   She is _____ daughter.

   She is also _____ daughter.

3. Kayla is _____ daughter.

   She is also _____ daughter.

   She is _____ granddaughter.

   She is also _____ granddaughter.

4. Jeff is _____ husband.

   He is _____ brother.

   He is also _____ father.

James Sarah Annie Jeff Kayla Carol

C Change the sentences. Use *his*, *her*, or *their*.

1. Pablo is Marina's brother. *Pablo is her brother.* _____

2. My grandfather's house is small. _____

3. My sister's name is Akiko. _____

4. John's parents are doctors. _____

5. My brothers' names are Raul and Emilio. _____

6. I'm Jose's cousin. _____

7. This is my parents' car. _____

VOCABULARY AND GRAMMAR

A Unscramble the letters to write words.

1. emridra _____

2. ginsel _____

3. bdhnusa _____

4. derynifob _____

5. gsniee monoese _____

6. rengridfli _____

B Complete the sentences with words from **A**.

1. My sister met her _____ at work. His name's Felipe.

2. She's not married, but she's _____.

3. Their cousin is getting _____ soon.

4. Do you have a _____?

5. His younger sisters are _____.

6. Where does your _____ work?

C Complete the sentences with *'s got* or *'ve got*.

1. I _____ class on Monday and Thursday.

2. My sister _____ three children.

3. He _____ a brother who's a doctor.

4. They _____ a lot of work to do before class.

5. We _____ a great idea.

6. My uncle _____ a new car.

D Unscramble the words to make a conversation.

1. old / you / are / how

   A: _____?

2. years / I / am / old / 23

   B: _____.

3. you / single / are

   A: _____?

4. no, / got / wife / I've / a

   B: _____.

5. have / do / children / you / any

   A: _____?

6. two / I / children / have

   B: _____.

READING AND WRITING

A What's your opinion? Circle your answers.

1. Large families are happy families.	Yes	Maybe	No
2. Children need a brother or sister.	Yes	Maybe	No
3. Single people are very lucky.	Yes	Maybe	No
4. I want a lot of children.	Yes	Maybe	No

B Read the article about Liza J. Smith. Then complete the sentences with words from the box.

Star Spotter Magazine   62

This week in Star Talk . . .   **Star Talk**

Actress Liza J. Smith talks about her four husbands!

Yes, it's true… I married my first husband in 1996 in London. I was very young. Nigel and I have two sons: Ian and Derek. They live in England.

I married Raymond in Los Angeles in 2004. He's an actor—a bad actor! But we've got a beautiful daughter. Her name is Lily. She lives with her father and her stepmother.

In 2010, I married James in Sydney. We have two children: Jason and Jenny. James is a good man, but he's not the right husband for me. James's new wife is a famous scientist.

I'm so happy now! I have a wonderful life with my husband, Pierre. I married Pierre in 2018. This is true love! We've got a new baby. His name is Luc. I live in a big house in Switzerland with Pierre, my baby, Jason and Jenny, and Pierre's three daughters. Their names are Zelda, Zenia, and Zora. I love big families!

---

brother	daughter	father	mother	sister	son

1. Zora is Zelda's _____.

2. Liza is Lily's _____.

3. Ian is Liza's _____.

4. Pierre is Zora's _____.

5. Derek is Ian's _____.

6. Zenia is Liza's _____.

C Read the paragraphs. Then complete the sentences with possessive nouns.

> One of the most famous American movie directors is Francis Ford Coppola. Some of his most famous films are the three *Godfather* movies. But Coppola is not the only famous person in his family. His daughter is also a director. Her name is Sofia Coppola. Eleanor Coppola, Francis's wife and Sofia's mother, also works in film, often with her family. She made a film about the making of her husband's movie *Apocalypse Now*, and another about her daughter's movie *Marie Antoinette*. These three family members work behind the camera.
>
> Other members of this family are actors. Francis Ford Coppola's sister is Talia Shire. Some of her most famous roles are in the *Godfather* movies and *Rocky*. She plays Rocky's wife. Talia's son is Jason Schwartzman. He was in his cousin Sofia's movie *Marie Antoinette*. He often works on movies with another cousin, Sofia's brother, Roman. Another actor in the family is Nicolas Cage. (His real name is Nicolas Coppola.) Francis Ford and Eleanor Coppola are his uncle and aunt. Sofia and Roman are Nicolas's cousins.

1. The *Godfather* is one of Francis Ford _____ movies.

2. Francis Ford Coppola's _____ name is Sofia.

3. Sofia's _____ name is Eleanor.

4. Sofia's _____ name is Talia Shire.

5. Sofia's _____ name is Roman.

6. Talia's _____ name is Jason Schwartzman.

7. Jason's _____ names are Sofia and Roman Coppola, and Nicolas Cage.

8. Nicolas Cage's _____ name is Francis Ford Coppola.

D Write about a family in a movie or TV show. Who are the actors? What are the characters like?

_____

_____

_____

_____

_____

_____

_____

_____

7

TIME

A MY ROUTINE

VOCABULARY

A Write the times in numbers.

1. two forty-five	_____	**5.** eight o'clock	_____
2. one thirty	_____	**6.** a quarter to four	_____
3. five-fifteen	_____	**7.** five o'clock	_____
4. a quarter past ten	_____	**8.** half past nine	_____

B Match the times (1–8) with the clocks (a–h).

_____ **1.** six thirty

_____ **2.** a quarter to seven

_____ **3.** three ten

_____ **4.** twelve o'clock

_____ **5.** a quarter past eleven

_____ **6.** seven thirty

_____ **7.** four oh eight

_____ **8.** one forty-five

C Put the times of day in order from earliest to latest.

afternoon	evening	morning	night

_____ → _____ → _____ → _____

D What time do you do the following? Write the times in numbers and words.

1. eat dinner   *7: 30 / seven thirty* _____

2. wake up   _____

3. eat breakfast   _____

4. start English class   _____

5. finish English class   _____

6. watch your favorite TV show   _____

7. go to bed   _____

CONVERSATION

A Make suggestions. Use *How about . . . ?*, *Let's . . . ,* or *We could . . . .*

1. the Pizza Palace   *Let's have dinner at the Pizza Palace.*

2. that new horror movie   _____

3. swimming   _____

4. the Colombian restaurant   _____

5. a bike ride   _____

B Write answers with *I don't really . . . .*

1. Let's listen to some classical music.
   I don't really like classical music. _____

2. Let's watch a basketball game on TV.

   _____

3. Let's play tennis.

   _____

4. Let's see the new Jennifer Lawrence movie.

   _____

5. Let's eat at Tasca Restaurant.

   _____

6. Let's go shopping.

   _____

C Complete the conversations. There can be more than one right answer.

1. **A:** (1.) _____ go to the new Chinese restaurant.
   B: I don't (2.) _____.
   A: (3.) _____ Japanese food.
   B: (4.) _____ sounds (5.) _____!

2. **A:** (1.) _____ play (2.) _____.
   B: Hmm. (3.) _____.
   A: Then (4.) _____.
   B: OK, (5.) _____!

D Write your own conversation.

A: _____

B: _____

A: _____

B: _____

GRAMMAR

A Complete the sentences. Use *in*, *on*, or *at*.

1. Marco has English class _____ Thursday _____ 8:00 _____ the morning.

2. I work in a department store every day _____ the afternoon.

3. I always watch the news on TV _____ 7:00 _____ the evening.

4. _____ Saturdays, I always get up _____ 10:00.

5. Hassan visits his grandparents _____ Friday evenings.

6. Our math exam is _____ 4:30 _____ Tuesday.

B Look at the work schedule. Write sentences about these people.

	Monday	**Tuesday**	**Wednesday**	**Thursday**	**Friday**	**Saturday**
morning	Mimi	Jack	Jack	Jack	Jack	Anika
afternoon	David	Nadia	Mimi	Vitor	David	Anika
evening	Sam	x	Sam	x	Sam	Sam

1. David *He works in the afternoon on Mondays and Fridays.* _____

2. Mimi _____

3. Nadia _____

4. Anika _____

5. Sam _____

6. Vitor _____

7. Jack _____

C Complete the sentences with *on*, *in*, *at*, or *from . . . to*.

1. My English class is _____ 10:00 _____ 11:30 on Tuesdays and Thursdays.

2. I usually study _____ the afternoon.

3. I go home _____ 4:00.

4. I watch TV _____ 11:00 _____ midnight.

5. I don't study at all _____ Saturdays.

6. The show starts _____ 7:30.

7. The meeting is _____ the morning.

8. I don't have to work _____ the weekend.

D Read the answers. Then write *when* questions.

1. Q: *When is your favorite show on TV?* _____   A: My favorite show is on TV at 6:00 tonight.

2. Q: _____   A: My piano lesson is at 3:00 on Tuesday.

3. Q: _____   A: The test is at 2:00 on Friday.

4. Q: _____   A: The party is on Saturday night.

5. Q: _____   A: Farid's dance class is at noon tomorrow.

VOCABULARY AND GRAMMAR

A Write the weekend activities in the correct category.

| a bike ride | classmates | friends | school | shopping | swimming | a walk |

go	go to	go for	go out with

B Write lists of weekend activities. Use phrases from **A** and your own ideas.

I love to . . . 😊	It's OK to . . . 😐	I don't like to . . . ☹

C Read the answers. Write questions using *what*, *when*, *where*, or *who*.

1. **Q:** *What* _____

   A: On weekends, I study and see my friends.

2. **Q:** *Where* _____

   A: I live on Lake Street.

3. **Q:** *Who* _____

   A: I go dancing with my girlfriend.

4. **Q:** *When* _____

   A: I go to the gym at 10:00.

5. **Q:** *Where* _____

   A: I go to Baxter School.

READING AND WRITING

A A reporter is interviewing a famous tennis player. Read the interview and write the questions from the box in the correct spaces.

> Who do you live with?
>
> When do you relax?
>
> What do you do in your free time?
>
> Where do you live?
>
> What do you do on Saturdays?
>
> What do you do in the evenings?

Reporter: _____?

    Evans: I have a big house in California. The weather is very good for tennis.

Reporter: _____?

    Evans: I live with my dog. His name is Racket.

Reporter: _____?

    Evans: Free time? What's that? I work out at the gym in the morning for two hours. Then I play tennis for four hours.

Reporter: _____?

    Evans: At night, I watch sports on TV, and I answer emails. People ask me a lot of tennis questions.

Reporter: _____?

    Evans: I work hard on Saturdays. I play tennis for six hours and then I watch tennis videos.

Reporter: _____?

    Evans: I relax on Sundays. I have lunch with my parents and see my girlfriend.

B Circle **T** for *true* or **F** for *false*. Rewrite the false sentences to make them true.

1. Evans relaxes every day.   **T**   **F**

_____

2. He spends time with his parents on Saturdays.   **T**   **F**

_____

3. He answers questions about tennis.   **T**   **F**

_____

4. He lives with his parents.   **T**   **F**

_____

C Read this interview. Complete the sentences with *in*, *on*, or *at*.

> **A:** What do you do to relax?
>
> **B:** Well, **(1.)** _____ the evening, I play with my children. I'm a single parent. My daughter is six, and my son is three. They go to bed **(2.)** _____ 8:00. Then I read or watch movies. **(3.)** _____ Mondays and Wednesdays **(4.)** _____ 7:00, I take an art class. I'm learning how to draw.
>
> **A:** And what do you do **(5.)** _____ weekends?
>
> **B:** I usually work **(6.)** _____ Friday and Saturday nights. I have a concert or a live TV show. **(7.)** _____ the afternoon, I practice singing. **(8.)** _____ the morning, I sleep very late. My children stay with their grandmother **(9.)** _____ the weekends.

D Imagine you are a famous person. Answer the reporter's questions.

Name of famous person:

_____

Reporter: What do you do in the evening?

_____

_____

_____

_____

_____

_____

Reporter: What do you do on weekends?

_____

_____

_____

_____

_____

_____

8

SPECIAL OCCASIONS

A TAKING TIME OFF

VOCABULARY

A Complete the names of the months.

1. __ a __

2. __ __ __ __ h

3. __ __ __ e

4. __ __ __ y

5. A __ __ __ __ __

6. __ __ v __ __ e __

7. F __ __ __ u __ __ __

8. A __ __ __ l

9. S __ __ __ __ __ __ __ r

10. __ __ __ u __ __ __

11. O __ __ __ __ __ r

12. D __ __ __ __ __ __ __

B Unscramble the letters to write the names of the seasons.

1. ientwr   _____

2. mesrmu   _____

3. lalf   _____

4. pgnsir   _____

C Write the ordinal numbers for the days of the months. Follow the example.

1. 5/10   _May tenth_____

2. 2/16   _____

3. 8/23   _____

4. 11/9   _____

5. 10/1   _____

6. 4/5   _____

7. 7/4   _____

8. 6/27   _____

9. 3/10   _____

D Write down five important holidays in your country. Use numbers and then words.

1. _New Year's Day_____   _1/1_____   _January first_____

2. _____   _____   _____

3. _____   _____   _____

4. _____   _____   _____

5. _____   _____   _____

CONVERSATION

A Number the sentences in order to make a conversation.

_____ It's a holiday in the United States.

_____ Oh, ok. No, I don't have plans.
Do people do anything special?

_____ Really? When is it?

_____ Do you have plans for Memorial Day?

_____ Yes. People visit memorials or
participate in parades. They also get
together with friends and family and
have barbecues.

_____ I have no idea. What's Memorial Day?

_____ It's the last Monday in May.

B Unscramble the words to make questions and statements.

1. is / holiday / a / today

_____?

2. last / in / Friday / the / June / it's

_____.

3. do / on / do / people / what / day / this

_____?

4. sure / not / I'm / is / it / when

_____.

5. St. Patrick's Day / on / March / is / 17

_____.

C Match the expressions with the percentages.

_____ 1. I'm not sure.   a. certain

_____ 2. It's on May 20th.   b. less certain

_____ 3. Maybe   c. not certain at all

D Write a conversation about a holiday.

A: _____

B: _____

A: _____

B: _____

A: _____

B: _____

GRAMMAR

A Unscramble the words to write questions.

1. chess / who / you / with / do / play

   _____?

2. where / from / Niko / does / come

   _____?

3. what / are / class / you / in / English

   _____?

4. school / do / go / which / you / to

   _____?

5. is / letter / for / who / this

   _____?

6. do / who / you / time / with / spend

   _____?

7. are / looking / you / what / for

   _____?

8. what / live / you / street / on / do

   _____?

9. with / are / they / who

   _____?

10. time / at / is / what / movie / the

    _____?

B Complete each question with a preposition from the box.

about	at	in	on	to	with

1. What time is your party _____?
2. Who do Tanya and Ena live _____?
3. What day is Father's Day _____?
4. What month is your birthday _____?
5. What music are you listening _____?
6. Who are you talking _____?

C Write sentences with *in* or *on*.

1. my birthday / July 10 *My birthday is on July tenth.* _____
2. our vacation / summer _____
3. our party / New Year's Day _____
4. Labor Day / September _____
5. Valentine's Day / winter _____
6. International Women's Day / March 8 _____

B BIG EVENTS

VOCABULARY AND GRAMMAR

A Complete the paragraph. Use the words in the box.

attend	celebrate	compete	event	every	place	traditional

Thousands of people **(1.)** _____ the Sundance Film Festival. It takes

(2.) _____ in Park City, Utah, **(3.)** _____ year. This festival is the biggest

(4.) _____ of the year in Park City. Directors show their work and **(5.)** _____

to win film awards. Big, expensive parties are a **(6.)** _____ part of the festival where

actors and filmmakers **(7.)** _____ the success of their films.

B Match the things that go together.

_____ **1.** The Olympics is an example.   **a.** film festival

_____ **2.** It shows movies.   **b.** food festival

_____ **3.** It has singers.   **c.** sports event

_____ **4.** You can try traditional dishes there.   **d.** music festival

C Read the answer in each conversation. Then complete the questions with *When* or *How long*.

1. A: _____ is the parade?

   B: It's on February 9.

2. A: _____ is your vacation?

   B: Two weeks.

3. A: _____ do you go on vacation?

   B: I go in late August every year.

4. A: _____ is the movie?

   B: It's about two and a half hours long.

5. A: _____ do you work on Fridays?

   B: I work for six hours.

D Complete the sentences with *in*, *on*, *from . . . to*, or *for*.

1. They play soccer _____ two hours every day.

2. My English course lasts _____ two months.

3. The party is _____ 9:00 _____ 12:00.

4. I don't have classes _____ Sunday.

5. School closes _____ the summer.

6. I stay with my grandparents _____ two weeks every year.

READING AND WRITING

A Read the article and write the letter of the photo next to the holiday it shows.

Today's Question:

What's your favorite holiday? Why?

_____ 1. I'm from Frankfurt, Germany, and Christmas is my favorite holiday. I love our traditional Christmas tree. It's so beautiful. We also give lots of gifts and sing Christmas songs.

—Karin Schmidt

_____ 2. I live in Daegu, Korea, and my favorite holiday is called *Chuseok*. On this holiday, it's traditional for people to go to the city they come from. They visit their families, eat special foods, and talk for hours. I like Chuseok because I see all of my cousins then.

—Park
Kyoung-Mi

_____ 3. I'm from Rio de Janeiro in Brazil. My favorite holiday is Carnival. It lasts for four days. People wear beautiful clothes. They eat, drink, and dance in a parade with their friends. It's my favorite holiday because I love the traditional clothes and I love the music of Carnival.

—Paulo Amaral

B Fill in the chart with information from **A**.

Name	Country	Favorite holiday	Why?
1.			
2.			*She sees all of her cousins.*
3.			

C Read about a favorite holiday. Cross out the eight spelling mistakes. Rewrite the misspelled words correctly on the lines below. Use the example to help you.

I'm from Oslo, Norway. My favorite ~~holliday~~ takes palce evry year on May 17. That's our National Day here in Norway. We sing special songs for this day. All the cities have big parades. The schoolchildren preform songs, and their parents watch. The children also go to the houses of older people and sing for them. The largest parade is in Oslo. About 100,000 people atend this parad. The people wear traditionel clothes. For me, it's the most interesting evint of the year.

1. ___holiday___   3. _____   5. _____   7. _____

2. _____   4. _____   6. _____   8. _____

D Write about your favorite holiday. Why do you like it? What special activities do you do on that day?

My favorite holiday is . . . _____

_____

_____

_____

_____

_____

_____

_____

9
TOGETHER

A ROOMMATES

VOCABULARY

A Complete each sentence with the correct form of *do* or *make*.

1. Please don't _____ noise while I _____ my homework.

2. Every morning, I _____ my bed.

3. I always _____ my own laundry.

4. I usually _____ my own lunch for school.

5. Sometimes my sister _____ her own breakfast.

6. I usually _____ the dishes after dinner.

7. My mother usually _____ dinner for the family.

8. My family usually _____ some chores on Saturday morning.

B Read and complete the paragraph. Use the simple present or the present continuous form of *make* or *do*.

My mother has a job, so my brother and I help her at home. We **(1.)** _____ a lot of chores every day. First, my brother **(2.)** _____ breakfast and **(3.)** _____ the beds. Then I **(4.)** _____ the breakfast dishes. My brother takes out the garbage. Right now, I **(5.)** _____ the laundry. I **(6.)** _____ my homework at the same time.

C Who does each job in your house? Write complete sentences.

does the dishes   _____

_____

makes breakfast   _____

_____

takes out the garbage   _____

_____

does the laundry   _____

_____

cleans the bathroom   _____

_____

makes dinner   _____

_____

CONVERSATION

A Unscramble the words to make sentences.

1. sorry / about / I'm / that _____

2. worry / it / don't / about _____

3. I'm / sorry / really _____

4. OK / that's _____

5. all / right / that's _____

B Write each sentence from **A** in the correct row.

Making an apology	
Responding to an apology	

C Number the sentences in order to make a conversation.

_____ Don't worry about it. Have fun!

_____ Hey Jin.

_____ Not much. Can you do the dishes tonight?

_____ Hi. What's up Fatima?

_____ Yes, I have a book club meeting, so I can't do the dishes. Thank you so much.

_____ Sure. No problem. Are you going out?

D Write a conversation in which someone apologizes.

A: _____

B: _____

A: _____

B: _____

A: _____

B: _____

A: _____

B: _____

GRAMMAR

A Look at the survey and write sentences. Follow the example.

	Matt	Jai	Tim	Anya
Do you get up early?	sometimes	always	often	never
Do you eat breakfast?	always	never	always	usually
Are you late for class?	sometimes	hardly ever	never	sometimes
Do you drink coffee?	often	sometimes	never	never
Are you a good student?	sometimes	sometimes	usually	usually

1. Anya / get up early *Anya never gets up early.*

2. Matt / drink coffee _____

3. Matt and Tim / eat breakfast _____

4. Anya / good student _____

5. Tim and Anya / drink coffee _____

6. Anya and Matt / late for class _____

7. Jai / eat breakfast _____

8. Jai / late for class _____

9. Tim / get up early _____

B Answer the questions using complete sentences and frequency adverbs.

1. Do you get up early? _____

2. Do you eat junk food? _____

3. Are you late for class? _____

4. Do you drink tea? _____

5. Do you go to bed late? _____

6. Do you eat breakfast at home? _____

7. Do you play video games? _____

8. Do you go camping? _____

C Write sentences that are true for you.

1. usually *Usually I have a test on Friday.*

2. never *I never eat junk food.*

3. always _____

4. hardly ever _____

5. sometimes _____

6. often _____

7. never _____

8. usually _____

VOCABULARY AND GRAMMAR

A Complete the sentences with the words and expressions in the box.

| best friends | friendship | get along | hang out | keep in touch | make friends | meet |

1. Manuel isn't popular at work because he doesn't _____ well with others.

2. They _____ through social media and video calls.

3. Marco and his friends _____ together on the weekends.

4. Amelia and Leticia are _____. They spend a lot of time together.

5. Is social media a good way to _____ new people?

6. New students often _____ with their classmates.

7. Our _____ is very important to me.

B Complete the questions with *What, Where, Who,* or *How long*.

1. **A:** _____ does he live? **B:** In Mexico City.

2. **A:** _____ is the movie? **B:** It's at the Rialto Theater.

3. **A:** _____ is the event? **B:** It's from 1:00 to 4:00.

4. **A:** _____ is in the bag? **B:** My books.

5. **A:** _____ is Luis? **B:** He's my friend from the gym.

6. **A:** _____ do you study? **B:** I always study at home.

7. **A:** _____ does summer vacation last? **B:** Usually two months.

8. **A:** _____ do you hang out with friends? **B:** We usually hang out on the weekends.

C Unscramble the words to make questions. Then write answers that are true for you.

1. you / where / do / go / class / after _____?

_____

2. eat / lunch / what / do / you / for _____?

_____

3. what / fun / do / for / you / do _____?

_____

4. you / where / to / do / school / go _____?

_____

5. is / how / class / English / long / your _____?

_____

6. is / your / who / teacher _____?

_____

READING AND WRITING

A What's your friendship style? Read the questions and answer for yourself.

1.	It's not a good idea to live with friends.	**Agree**	**Disagree**
2.	It's important to have close friends at school.	**Agree**	**Disagree**
3.	The best friends are old friends.	**Agree**	**Disagree**
4.	It's easy to make new friends.	**Agree**	**Disagree**
5.	My online friends aren't close friends.	**Agree**	**Disagree**
6.	I keep in touch with friends who live far away.	**Agree**	**Disagree**

B Read the article.

> When I'm away at college, I don't keep in touch with my friends at home. I don't have time to write emails or call them. I'm too busy with classes, playing soccer, and hanging out with my new friends. But during school vacations and the summer, I hang out with my old friends every day. Our friendship never changes.
>
> —Esteban
>
> I get along well with people, but it's hard for me to make close friends. I'm shy, so I don't like meeting new people. I want to make new friends here at school, but it's not easy. I miss my old friends at home.
>
> —Gloria
>
> I have a full-time job now. I get along with my coworkers, but I don't have any close friends at work. Part of the reason for this is that my coworkers and I are different ages. A lot of them are older than me. Some of them are married and have children. Usually they can't hang out after work or on the weekend.
>
> —Eduardo

C Circle **T** for *true* or **F** for *false*. Rewrite the false sentences to make them true.

1. Esteban has new friends at school and old friends at home.	**T**	**F**
_____		
2. Esteban keeps in touch with his friends at home all the time.	**T**	**F**
_____		
3. Gloria doesn't get along well with people.	**T**	**F**
_____		
4. Gloria doesn't enjoy meeting new people.	**T**	**F**
_____		
5. It's not easy for Gloria to make new friends.	**T**	**F**
_____		
6. Eduardo doesn't get along with his coworkers.	**T**	**F**
_____		
7. Eduardo's coworkers have time to hang out after work.	**T**	**F**
_____		

D Read the paragraph. Fill in the blanks with the words in the box.

| best | friendship | hang out | keep in touch | make friends | old friends | roommate |

My mother's best friend is Nancy, her **(1.)** _____ from college. They met when they were 18, and that was over 20 years ago! They're still **(2.)** _____ friends. Now they live far away from each other, but they **(3.)** _____ by talking on the phone often. They also text and email each other all the time. And they **(4.)** _____ in person several times a year. Of course, both of them **(5.)** _____ with new people they meet, such as coworkers and neighbors, but their **(6.)** _____ is very special because they are **(7.)** _____.

E Write about an old friend. What is your friend like? How do you keep in touch? When do you see each other? What do you like to do together?

_____

_____

_____

_____

_____

_____

_____

F Write about a new friend. What is your friend like? When do you hang out? What do you usually do together?

_____

_____

_____

_____

_____

_____

_____

10

HOME

A   AT HOME

VOCABULARY

A   Match the word with the description.

___d___ 1. shower

_____ 2. sofa

_____ 3. dining area

_____ 4. closet

_____ 5. apartment

_____ 6. bedroom

_____ 7. living room

_____ 8. bathroom

_____ 9. kitchen

a. You wash dishes there.

b. You eat dinner there.

c. There is a sofa there.

d. You wash your hair there.

e. You sleep there.

f. There is a shower there.

g. One or more people can sit on this.

h. You keep clothes there.

i. You live there.

B   Complete the sentences. Use the words in the box.

apartment	bathtub	chair	closet	kitchen	table

1. Please put the clean clothes in the bedroom _____.

2. Put your dirty dishes in the _____.

3. There are four rooms in my new _____.

4. We need another _____ at the table. My uncle is coming to dinner.

5. Please put the plates and cups on the _____.

6. Our new bathroom has a large _____.

C   What items are in these rooms in your house? Make a list for each room.

Living Room	Kitchen	Bedroom

CONVERSATION

A Complete the conversation with the words in the box.

apartment	it's	there's	you're kidding
are you serious	the rent is	there's no	

Max: Hi, Tranh.

Tranh: Hi, Max. Come in!

Max: Thanks. So, this is your new place. Wow, nice **(1.)** _____!

Tranh: Yeah, and **(2.)** _____ $600 a month.

Max: **(3.)** _____? 600? That's cheap.

Tranh: Yeah, and there's an extra bedroom.

Max: **(4.)** _____! This apartment is huge!

Tranh: Yeah, I know. **(5.)** _____ a great apartment. **(6.)** _____ just one problem.

Max: What's that?

Tranh: **(7.)** _____ air conditioning.

B Complete the conversation about this picture. Use your own ideas.

You: Hi, _____.

Your friend: Hi, _____. Come in.

You: _____. So, this is your new _____.

Your friend: Yeah, and it's only _____.

You: You're kidding! _____? That's _____.

Your friend: Yeah, and there's _____.

You: Really?

Your friend: It's true. It's a great _____. There's just one _____.

You: What's that?

Your friend: There's no _____.

GRAMMAR

A Write questions and answers about the living room in this photo. Follow the example.

1. _____Is there_____ a TV?   _____No, there isn't._____

2. _____ a sofa?   _____

3. _____ a table?   _____

4. _____ a dining area?   _____

5. _____ a chair?   _____

6. _____ a closet?   _____

B Write sentences about your bedroom. Use *there is* and *there are*. Follow the example.

1. *There is a bed.* _____

2. _____

3. _____

4. _____

5. _____

6. _____

7. _____

C Make questions using the words and *how many*. Then write answers that are true for you. Follow the example.

1. rooms / your apartment *How many rooms are in your apartment?* _____
   There are four rooms in my apartment. _____

2. people / your family _____
   _____

3. pages / this book _____
   _____

4. students / your class _____
   _____

5. windows / your bedroom _____
   _____

6. units / this book _____
   _____

7. shirts / your closet _____
   _____

8. chairs / your kitchen _____
   _____

VOCABULARY AND GRAMMAR

A Circle the correct word in each sentence.

1. Look at those **white** / **blue** clouds.
2. The leaves of plants are usually **pink** / **green**.
3. The sky is **brown** / **blue**.
4. Linda's eyes are **brown** / **yellow**.
5. My grandfather's hair is **blue** / **gray**.
6. When you mix red and white, you get **purple** / **pink**.
7. A person's eyes are never **orange** / **brown**.
8. When you mix black and white, you get **green** / **gray**.
9. In the fall, the leaves on the trees turn **blue** / **orange**.
10. Dogs don't have **pink** / **brown** hair.
11. The sun looks **black** / **yellow**.

B Rewrite the underlined sentences correctly. Use *very* or *too*. If the sentence is correct, write *C*.

1. I worked ten hours today. <u>I'm very tired to go out.</u>
  I'm too tired to go out.

2. <u>Lisa is very nice.</u> She always helps people.
  _____

3. Vadim can't stop jumping around. <u>He's very excited to sit down.</u>
  _____

4. Magda studied a lot. <u>She got a too good grade on the test.</u>
  _____

5. <u>Ali is very rich.</u> His family has a lot of money.
  _____

6. <u>The baby is too young.</u> She's only six days old.
  _____

7. Fatima is 104 years old. <u>She's too old to climb big mountains.</u>
  _____

8. Elementary school students can't vote. <u>They're very young.</u>
  _____

9. I can't go to the party tonight. <u>I'm very busy to go.</u>
  _____

READING AND WRITING

A Scan the article very quickly. Who writes about each of these colors?

1. yellow   _____

2. blue   _____

3. green   _____

B Read the magazine article.

How the Color of Our Walls Affects Us

Emily Lawson
Interior Decorator

Blue is one of my favorite colors. **It** can really change how a room feels. Light blue walls, like the color of the sky, make people feel calm. However, dark blue, like navy, has a very different effect. **It** often makes people feel sad and depressed.[1] Most decorators love light blue, but **others** can't stand it.

Fabio Pessoa
Psychologist

I tell all my clients to avoid painting their rooms yellow. This color seems to stimulate the nervous system. Babies cry more in a yellow room, and people are more likely to lose their temper there than in blue or green rooms. Some scientists also think that it causes the eyes to get tired faster when reading.

Ichiyo Mori
Office Manager

I always paint the walls in the office where I work light green. It helps people feel relaxed. Researchers say that the color green can help people read better. If you put transparent[2] green paper over the page of a book, you will read faster. That's good in an office, too.

[1]If someone is **depressed**, they feel very sad.
[2]If something is **transparent**, you can see through it.

C Look at the Emily Lawson section of the text. Find the meaning of each pronoun.

1. The first word _it_ means _____.

2. The second word _it_ means _____.

3. The word _others_ means other _____.

my bedroom

D Read the description of an apartment. Circle the names of rooms. Underline the names of colors.

> I love my apartment. The living room is a big, square room. I painted it yellow. There is a
> blue sofa. Across from it are two big red chairs. There's a white plastic table between the
> sofa and the chairs. The dining table is in the dining area. It is red. My bedroom is very calm
> and relaxing. The walls are gray. There are windows on two walls, so the room is always
> very bright. The kitchen walls are white. The refrigerator and other appliances are white, too.
> There's a big table with chairs in the middle of the room. I always keep some yellow flowers
> on the table.

E Reread **D**. Then rewrite the description of the apartment. Make it a place you would like to live in.
Change the rooms, furniture, and colors to ones you like. You can add new items if you wish.

_____

_____

_____

_____

_____

_____

_____

11

CLOTHING

A SHOPPING

VOCABULARY

A Unscramble the letters to write clothing words.

1. k i t s r _____skirt_____
2. s e r s d _____
3. l s e h e _____
4. t a c k e j _____
5. e i t _____

6. s e a n j _____
7. e l o b s u _____
8. s n d l a s a _____
9. f u r i n o m _____
10. t u s i _____

11. T - s r t h i _____
12. o k c s s _____
13. p n a s t _____
14. t h a _____
15. a n s e r s k e _____

B Write the clothing words in the correct column.

| boots | heels | pants | scarf | skirt | socks |
| gloves | jeans | sandals | shorts | sneakers | tie |

For Your Neck	For Your Feet	For Your Legs	For Your Hands

C Describe the clothing that you are wearing now. Write the color of each item.

1. *I'm wearing brown boots.* _____
2. _____
3. _____
4. _____
5. _____
6. _____
7. _____

CONVERSATION

A Complete the conversations. There is more than one possible answer.

1. **Clerk:** (1.) _____ you?

   Ming: Yes, (2.) _____. I'm (3.) _____ for a gift for a friend.

   Clerk: Well, (4.) _____ these beautiful sweaters.

   Ming: How much (5.) _____?

   Clerk: Fifty dollars each.

   Ming: I'll think (6.) _____.

   Clerk: We also have this scarf for fifteen dollars.

   Ming: It's perfect! I'll (7.) _____.

2. **Clerk:** Can I (1.) _____?

   Beatriz: Oh, yeah, (2.) _____. I'm (3.) _____ a gift for my brother. He's moving to Canada and needs winter clothes.

   Clerk: Well, (4.) _____ these gloves. They're perfect for cold weather.

   Beatriz: How much (5.) _____?

   Clerk: Thirty dollars.

   Beatriz: I'll think (6.) _____.

   Clerk: You can buy these warm winter socks for five dollars.

   Beatriz: They're nice. (7.) _____.

3. **Clerk:** Good morning! Can I help you?

   Claudia: Yes, (1.) _____. I'm (2.) _____ for a gift for my dad.

   Clerk: Well, we have this nice wool hat.

   Claudia: It's very nice. How much is it?

   Clerk: Seventy dollars.

   Claudia: Seventy dollars? OK, I'll think (3.) _____.

   Clerk: We also have these nice ties.

   Claudia: Oh, I like those. How much (4.) _____?

   Clerk: These are thirty dollars. And those bright ones are twenty-five dollars.

   Claudia: Perfect. (5.) _____ one of each.

B Write a conversation between you and a clerk in a clothing store.

Clerk: _____

You: _____

Clerk: _____

You: _____

Clerk: _____

You: _____

Clerk: _____

You: _____

GRAMMAR

A Unscramble the words to make sentences.

1. jeans / want / you / buy / do / these / to
   Do you want to buy these jeans _____?

2. has / suit / he / new / a

   _____.

3. gloves / to / we / buy / have

   _____.

4. sneakers / want / he / new / doesn't

   _____.

5. the party / have / do / dress up / we / to / for

   _____?

6. buy / he / mother / to / scarf / wants / a / his / for

   _____.

7. outside / has / wear / to / she / winter boots

   _____.

B Circle the correct words.

1. I don't have boots. I **have** / **have to** buy some.
2. I don't **want** / **want to** go shopping today.
3. My sister **has** / **has to** three pairs of heels.
4. They **want** / **want to** some new clothes.
5. We **have** / **have to** a lot of clothing stores in our town.
6. Do you **want** / **want to** get new shoes?
7. Erica **doesn't want** / **doesn't want to** any new clothes.
8. You **don't have** / **don't have to** wear a suit to work.
9. The store clerk **has** / **has to** work all day.
10. My mother **wants** / **wants to** a new jacket.
11. Amir **doesn't want** / **doesn't want to** wear a tie.

C Complete the sentences. Use your own ideas.

1. I want _____.
2. I want to _____.
3. My friend wants to _____.
4. My friend wants _____.
5. I have _____.
6. I have to _____.
7. My friend has to _____.
8. My friend has _____.

VOCABULARY AND GRAMMAR

A Complete the words in the paragraph.

The clothes you wear are part of your personal **(1.)** s __ y __ __. A lot of people like to wear **(2.)** c __ s __ __ l clothes while they are relaxing at home, like **(3.)** b __ __ __ y pants and **(4.)** l __ __ se sweaters. Many people think wearing **(5.)** t __ g __ __ clothing is uncomfortable, but others like it. People who work in an office sometimes have a business casual dress code and wear things like **(6.)** f __ t __ __ d shirts and pants, but nothing too **(7.)** d __ e __ __ y like heels or a tie. But some of us just love fashion, even at work, and **(8.)** dr __ __ __ u __ in a **(9.)** s __ __ l __ sh suit or dress every day. The great thing about style is everyone has their own!

B Identify the underlined word. Write *C* for *count noun* or *N* for *noncount noun*.

1. _____ I need to buy some new <u>clothes</u>.

2. _____ Where did you buy those <u>boots</u>?

3. _____ What is the <u>price</u> of that shirt?

4. _____ I don't like to wear <u>jewelry</u>.

5. _____ Wearing dressy clothes is a lot of <u>fun</u>.

6. _____ That <u>skirt</u> is really cool.

7. _____ New <u>clothing</u> can be expensive.

8. _____ Do you own a <u>pair</u> of sandals?

C Complete the sentences. Write *a*, *an*, *some*, or — (if no article is needed).

1. Did you study _____ history last night?

2. I like _____ clothing from Italy.

3. He is trying on _____ suit.

4. My mother lost _____ money.

5. I don't buy _____ dressy clothes often.

6. I have to get _____ new hat.

7. Do you want _____ stylish pair of sneakers?

8. I need _____ new shoes.

9. I have _____ old jacket.

READING AND WRITING

A Match the people with their clothes.

> **What are you wearing at work today?**
>
> a. I'm wearing old jeans and a casual shirt. I'm also wearing a hat and boots.
>
> b. I'm wearing a uniform: dark blue pants and a light blue shirt. I'm also wearing a big blue hat and black shoes.
>
> c. These are my team colors! I'm wearing a T-shirt, shorts, and socks. It's my uniform.
>
> d. I'm wearing a loose blue shirt and loose blue pants. My clothes are always very clean.
>
> e. Today I'm wearing a loose jacket, a blouse, and a skirt. I'm also wearing a pair of heels. My clothes are always very stylish.

1. A policeman _____

2. A model _____

3. A soccer player _____

4. A nurse _____

5. A cowboy _____

B Karissa is talking about her favorite party clothes. Complete the sentences with *a* or *an*. Write — if the sentences don't need an article.

I usually wear **(1.)** _____ stylish clothes to **(2.)** _____ party. I wear **(3.)** _____ fitted sweater and **(4.)** _____ dressy pants, or I sometimes wear **(5.)** _____ skirt. And I love **(6.)** _____ jewelry and **(7.)** _____ shoes. I always wear **(8.)** _____ old necklace my grandmother gave me, with heels or **(9.)** _____ pair of boots. I like to wear hats, too. My favorite hat to wear in the fall is **(10.)** _____ orange beret!

C What are your favorite party clothes? Write about them.

_____

_____

_____

_____

_____

_____

_____

D What clothes do you wear to exercise or play sports? Write about them.

_____

_____

_____

_____

_____

_____

JOBS

A WHAT DO YOU DO?

VOCABULARY

A Unscramble the letters to write the names of jobs.

1. c r o d o t _ _ _ _ _ _
2. r e w a l y _ _ _ _ _ _
3. w r a e t i _ _ _ _ _ _

4. g a n r a m e _ _ _ _ _ _ _
5. n i s t t i o c e p e r r _ _ _ _ _ _ i _ _ _ _ _
6. n i s t e d t _ _ _ _ _ _ _

B Complete the sentences. Use the words in the box.

| chef | engineer | hotel desk clerk | nurse | ~~receptionist~~ | software developer |
| dentist | flight attendant | lawyer | police officer | server | tour guide |

1. A _____receptionist_____ answers phones and greets people.
2. A _____ helps people check in to their rooms.
3. A _____ takes care of people's teeth.
4. A _____ helps keep people safe on the street.
5. A _____ brings food to your table in a restaurant.
6. A _____ takes care of patients in the hospital.
7. A _____ creates and works on computer programs.
8. A _____ works in an airplane.
9. A _____ helps people with legal problems.
10. A _____ shows visitors around a city or museum.
11. A _____ makes food in a restaurant.
12. An _____ develops technologies.

C Write the names of friends and family members. Write what job they do.

	Name	**Job**
1.	_____	_____
2.	_____	_____
3.	_____	_____
4.	_____	_____
5.	_____	_____

CONVERSATION

A Number the sentences in order to make a conversation.

_____ I'm a receptionist at a dentist's office.

_____ Hi, Sergio. I'm Hannah.

_____ Yeah, that's me. But I don't work in the library anymore.

__1__ Excuse me. Are you a friend of Samira's?

_____ Really? What do you do now?

_____ I like it a lot and the money's good.

_____ Yeah, hi. My name is Sergio.

_____ Hannah . . . I know you. You're Samira's friend, too, right? You work in the library.

_____ What's that like?

B A blogger is interviewing people about their jobs. Complete the interview. There may be more than one correct answer.

Blogger: (1.) _____?

Wendy: I'm Wendy Chang.

Blogger: Where (2.) _____?

Wendy: (3.) _____ Chang's Driving School.

Blogger: What (4.) _____?

Wendy: I'm a driving instructor. I teach people how to drive.

Blogger: (5.) _____?

Wendy: Yes, I like my job a lot.

Blogger: (6.) _____ your students like?

Wendy: They're very friendly.

C Write another interview. The blogger is interviewing your friend.

Blogger: _____

Your friend: _____

Blogger: _____

Your friend: _____

Blogger: _____

Your friend: _____

Blogger: _____

Your friend: _____

Blogger: _____

Your friend: _____

GRAMMAR

A Write questions about the sentences. Use *what* and *like*.

1. I have a new friend. Her name is Alice.
   What's she like?

2. I work in an animal hospital.
   _____

3. You haven't met my brother yet.
   _____

4. My art teacher is Mrs. Granger.
   _____

5. I work six days a week.
   _____

6. I've met a lot of new people this year.
   _____

B Write questions to complete the conversations. Use the word *like*.

1. **A:** Chris is a police officer.
   B: *What's that like?*
   A: Well, sometimes the work is dangerous.

2. **A:** I have a new roommate named Susana.
   B: _____
   A: She's nice, and she has a cool job as a software developer.

3. **A:** My cousins are from Mexico.
   B: _____
   A: They're very fun to be with.

4. **A:** My new doctor is only 26 years old.
   B: _____
   A: She's very smart.

5. **A:** I work at a candy factory.
   B: _____
   A: It's pretty boring most of the time.

6. **A:** My dad's a lawyer.
   B: _____
   A: It's a lot of work, but he enjoys it.

VOCABULARY AND GRAMMAR

A   Match the sentence parts.

_____ **1.** I want to get a job because

_____ **2.** A person with a full-time job

_____ **3.** She doesn't get any pay because she

_____ **4.** Rika works on weekends. She

_____ **5.** An internship

_____ **6.** Pedro's goal is

a. is a good way to get experience.

b. has a part-time job.

c. to get a job as an engineer.

d. I need to make money.

e. is doing an internship.

f. works over 35 hours a week.

B   Can you do these things? Write *yes* or *no*. What about your friend?

	Speak German	Drive a car	Paint	Swim
You				
Your friend				

C   Now write sentences with *can* or *can't*. Use the information from the chart above.

1. I _____ speak German.

2. _____

3. _____

4. _____

5. My friend _____ speak German.

6. _____

7. _____

8. _____

D   Samitha is an actor. She wants a job in a new movie. Complete the conversation.

Mrs. Lee: So, Samitha, **(1.)** _____ can you do? **(2.)** _____ _____ sing?

Samitha: Yes, I **(3.)** _____ sing a **(4.)** _____ bit, but not very well.

Mrs. Lee: Hmm. **(5.)** _____ _____ dance?

Samitha: I **(6.)** _____ dance, but not very **(7.)** _____.

Mrs. Lee: Hmm. So you **(8.)** _____ sing or dance very **(9.)** _____.
(10.) _____ you cry?

Samitha: Oh, yes! I **(11.)** _____ _____ very well.

Mrs. Lee: That's great! This is a sad, dramatic movie. You can do the job!

READING AND WRITING

A Marisol is writing an email to a new online friend about looking for a job. Scan her email and circle the three questions.

Dear Cho Sun-Ah,

Hello! My name is Marisol Torres. I'm from Guadalajara, Mexico. Nice to meet you! I have a problem: I am trying to find a summer job, but I don't know what I want to do!

I can speak Spanish, English, and a little French, so maybe I can find a job as a translator. Can you speak Spanish? I can teach you some words!

I love music, so maybe I can teach music. I can sing, and I can play the piano. I can also play the guitar and the violin, but not very well. Can you play any instruments?

I also like sports, so maybe I can work at a sports camp. I can play soccer and tennis, but I can't swim. I don't know how! Can you swim?

Please write soon! I'm waiting for your reply.

Your friend,

Marisol

B Now read the email. What can Marisol do? Check (✓) the correct answers.

	Yes	A little	No
sing			
speak French			
play tennis			
swim			
play the piano			
speak English			
play soccer			
play the violin			

C Read the reply to Marisol's email and fill in the blanks with the words in the box.

| can | can't | do | I'm | live | love | play | practice | speak | work |

Dear Marisol,

Thanks for your email. It's nice to get to know a new friend from another country! My name is Cho Sun-Ah. I **(1.)** _____ in Busan, South Korea. **(2.)** _____ a student at Busan National University of Education.

In my country, we **(3.)** _____ Korean. I study language education at the university. I **(4.)** _____ speak a little French and a little Japanese, but I can't speak Spanish.

I **(5.)** _____ music, too! I can't **(6.)** _____ any instruments, but I can sing.

I can swim a little, but I **(7.)** _____ play soccer or tennis. My favorite sport is baseball. **(8.)** _____ you like baseball?

I **(9.)** _____ as a tour guide in my city. It's a good way to **(10.)** _____ my English skills with visitors from around the world. Maybe this is a job you would like to try, too!

Your friend,

Sun-Ah

D Write to Marisol. Answer the three questions in Marisol's email and ask her three different questions.

Dear Marisol,

_____

_____

_____

_____

_____

_____

_____

_____

_____

Your friend,

_____